50+ Easy Popular Solos for Flute

GW00384947

Wise Publications
London/New York/Paris/Sydney/Copenhagen/Madrid

Exclusive Distributors:
Music Sales Limited
8/9 Frith Street, London W1V 5TZ, England.
Music Sales Pty Limited
120 Rothschild Avenue, Rosebery, NSW 2018, Australia.

Order No. AM932118
ISBN 0-7119-5193-4
This book © Copyright 1995 by Wise Publications

Cover design by Pearce Marchbank, Studio Twenty, London.

Printed in the United Kingdom by
Page Bros., Norwich, Norfolk.

Your Guarantee of Quality
As publishers, we strive to produce every book to the highest commercial standards.
The music has been freshly engraved and the book has been carefully designed to minimise
awkward page turns and to make playing from it a real pleasure.
Particular care has been given to specifying acid-free, neutral-sized paper made from pulps
which have not been elemental chlorine bleached. This pulp is from farmed sustainable forests
and was produced with special regard for the environment.
Throughout, the printing and binding have been planned to ensure a sturdy,
attractive publication which should give years of enjoyment.
If your copy fails to meet our high standards, please inform us and we will gladly replace it.

Music Sales' complete catalogue describes thousands of titles
and is available in full colour sections by subject,
direct from Music Sales Limited. Please state your areas of interest
and send a cheque/postal order for £1.50 for postage to:
Music Sales Limited, Newmarket Road,
Bury St. Edmunds, Suffolk IP33 3YB.

Also available...
50+ Easy Classical Solos for Flute
Easy-to-play melody line arrangements for flute,
complete with chord symbols in concert pitch.

Air from The Peasant Cantata *Bach*
Air in D Major from Orchestral Suite in D *Bach*
Ave Verum Corpus *Mozart*
Badinerie from Orchestral Suite in B Minor *Bach*
Bourrée *Bach*
But Who May Abide from 'Messiah' *Handel*
Dead March from 'Saul' *Handel*
Eine Kleine Nachtmusik:
1st Movement Theme *Mozart*
Eine Kleine Nachtmusik: Romance *Mozart*
Elvira Madigan: Theme from Piano Concerto
in C Major *Mozart*
German Dance *Beethoven*
Grand March from 'Aida' *Verdi*
He Shall Feed His Flock from 'Messiah' *Handel*
Hornpipe from Water Music *Handel*
I Know That My Redeemer Liveth
from 'Messiah' *Handel*
In Tears Of Grief from 'St Matthew Passion' *Bach*
Jesu, Joy Of Man's Desiring *Bach*
Largo from 'Xerxes' *Handel*
Let The Bright Seraphim from 'Samson' *Handel*
Lullaby *Mozart*
March from 'Scipione' *Handel*
Military March *Schubert*
Minuet in G *Bach*
Minuet in G *Beethoven*
Orchestral Suite in C: Bourrée No.1 *Bach*
Piano Concerto No.1 in C (Rondo) Op.15:
3rd Movement Theme *Beethoven*
Piano Sonata (Pathétique) Op.13:
2nd Movement Theme *Beethoven*
Pomp And Circumstance March No.1 *Elgar*
Radetzky March *Strauss*
Rondo Alla Turca from Sonata in A *Mozart*

Say Goodbye Now To Pastime from
'The Marriage Of Figaro' *Mozart*
See The Conquering Hero Comes from
'Judas Maccabaeus' *Handel*
Sheep May Safely Graze *Bach*
Sleepers, Wake! A Voice Is Calling *Bach*
Sonata in A: 1st Movement Theme *Mozart*
Sonata in C: 2nd Movement Theme *Mozart*
Sonata in C Minor: Last Movement Theme *Mozart*
Symphony in G Minor: Theme *Mozart*
Symphony No.1 in C Minor:
4th Movement Theme *Brahms*
Symphony No.3 in F: 3rd Movement Theme *Brahms*
Symphony No.5: Extract from
Andante Cantabile *Tchaikovsky*
Symphony No.5: Slow Movement Theme *Beethoven*
Symphony No.6 (Pastoral):
1st Movement Themes *Beethoven*
Symphony No.6 (Pathétique):
1st Movement Theme *Tchaikovsky*
Symphony No.7: 2nd Movement Theme *Beethoven*
Symphony No.9 in E Minor (From The New World):
2nd Movement Theme *Dvorák*
Symphony No.9 in E Minor (From The New World):
Finale *Dvorák*
Symphony No.9 (Ode To Joy):
Last Movement Theme *Beethoven*
Symphony No.94 in G (Surprise):
2nd Movement Theme *Haydn*
Tell Me Fair Ladies from
'The Marriage Of Figaro' *Mozart*
Tempo di Menuetto from Sonata
in G Op.49 No.2 *Beethoven*
The Manly Heart That Claims Our Duty
from 'The Magic Flute' *Mozart*

Order No. AM932063

A Whiter Shade Of Pale

Words & Music by Keith Reid & Gary Brooker

All I Have To Do Is Dream

Words & Music by Boudleaux Bryant

All The Way

Words by Sammy Cahn
Music by James Van Heusen

Am I That Easy To Forget

Words & Music by Carl Belew & W.S. Stevenson

Be-Bop-A-Lula

Words & Music by Gene Vincent & Sheriff Tex Davis

Blowin' In The Wind

Words & Music by Bob Dylan

Bridge Over Troubled Water

Words & Music by Paul Simon

Reflective

Buffalo Soldier

Words & Music by Noel Williams

Bye Bye Love

Words & Music by Felice & Boudleaux Bryant

Catch The Wind

Words & Music by Donovan

Diamonds Are A Girl's Best Friend

Words by Leo Robin
Music by Jule Styne

Didn't We Almost Have It All

Words & Music by Michael Masser & Will Jennings

Don't Cry For Me Argentina

Music by Andrew Lloyd Webber
Lyrics by Tim Rice

Downtown

Words & Music by Tony Hatch

Easy Lover

Music by Phil Collins, Philip Bailey & Nathan East
Words by Phil Collins

Every Breath You Take

Words & Music by Sting

Fly Me To The Moon (In Other Words)

Words & Music by Bart Howard

From Both Sides Now

Words & Music by Joni Mitchell

I Believe

Words & Music by Ervin Drake, Irvin Graham, Jimmy Shirl & Al Stillman

I Can See Clearly Now

Words & Music by Johnny Nash

Moderately with a beat

I Don't Know How To Love Him

Music by Andrew Lloyd Webber
Lyrics by Tim Rice

I Don't Want To Talk About It

Words & Music by Danny Whitten

I Know Him So Well

Words & Music by Benny Andersson, Tim Rice & Bjorn Ulvaeus

I Write The Songs

Words & Music by Bruce Johnston

I'd Like To Teach The World To Sing

Words & Music by Roger Cook, Roger Greenaway, Billy Backer & Billy Davis

If You Leave Me Now

Words & Music by Peter Cetera

33

Love Me Tender

Words & Music by Elvis Presley & Vera Matson

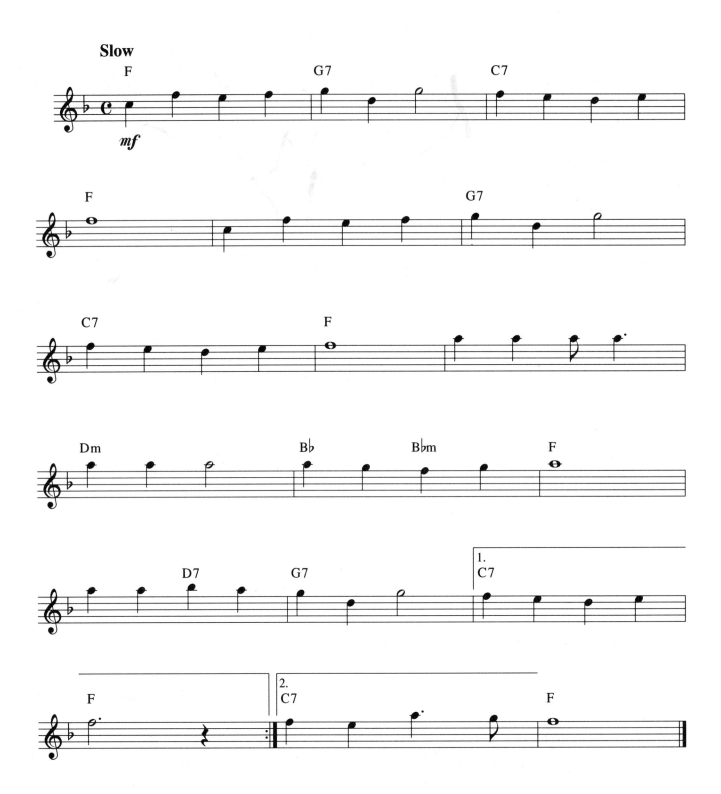

Memories Are Made Of This

Words & Music by Terry Gilkyson, Richard Dehr & Frank Miller

Mr Tambourine Man

Words & Music by Bob Dylan

Mull Of Kintyre

Words & Music by McCartney & Laine

Private Dancer

Words & Music by Mark Knopfler

Rocket Man

Words & Music by Elton John & Bernie Taupin

Release Me

Words & Music by Eddie Miller, Dub Williams, Robert Yount & Robert Harris

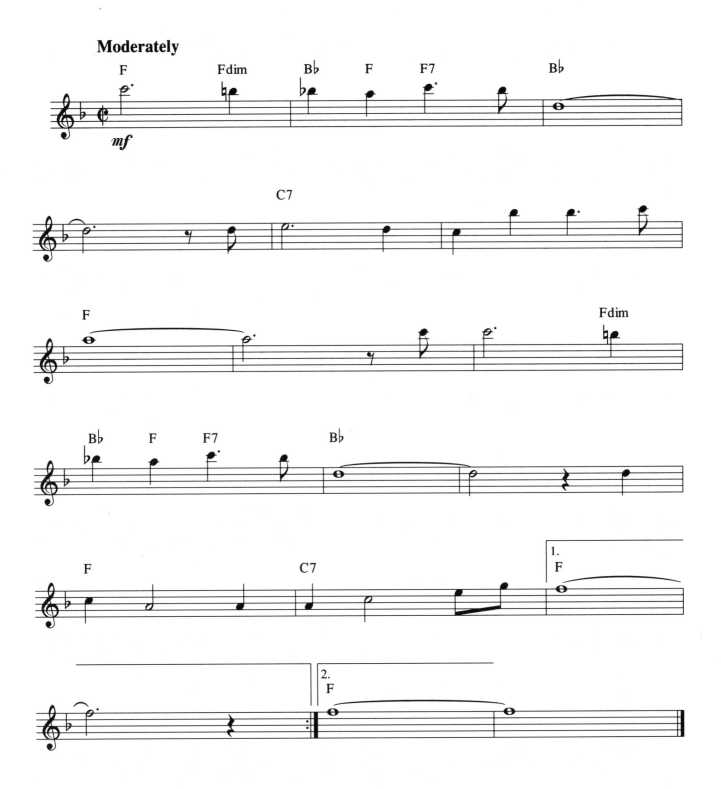

Sailing

Words & Music by Gavin Sutherland

Sometimes When We Touch

Words & Music by Dan Hill & Barry Mann

Spanish Eyes

Words by Charles Singleton, Eddie Snyder
Music by Bert Kaempfert

Take That Look Off Your Face

Words by Don Black
Music by Andrew Lloyd Webber

That Ole Devil Called Love

Words & Music by Doris Fisher & Allan Roberts

The Air That I Breathe

Words & Music by Albert Hammond & Mike Hazelwood

The Girl From Ipanema

(Garota De Ipanema)

Original Words by Vinicius De Moraes
English Lyric by Norman Gimbel
Music by Antonio Carlos Jobim

Medium bossa

The Great Pretender

Words & Music by Buck Ram

Moderately slow

Tie A Yellow Ribbon 'Round The Ole Oak Tree

Words & Music by Irwin Levine & L. Russell Brown

Too Much Heaven

Words & Music by Barry Gibb, Robin Gibb & Maurice Gibb

Those Were The Days

Words & Music by Gene Raskin

Tulips From Amsterdam

English Words by Gene Martyn Original Words by Neumann & Bader
Music by Ralf Arnie

Waltz tempo

Walk On By

Words by Hal David
Music by Burt Bacharach

We've Only Just Begun

Words by Paul Williams
Music by Roger Nichols

What I Did For Love

Words by Edward Kleban
Music by Marvin Hamlisch

Slowly

Without You

Words & Music by Peter Ham & Tom Evans

What's Love Got To Do With It

Words & Music by Graham Lyle & Terry Britten

Woman

Words & Music by John Lennon

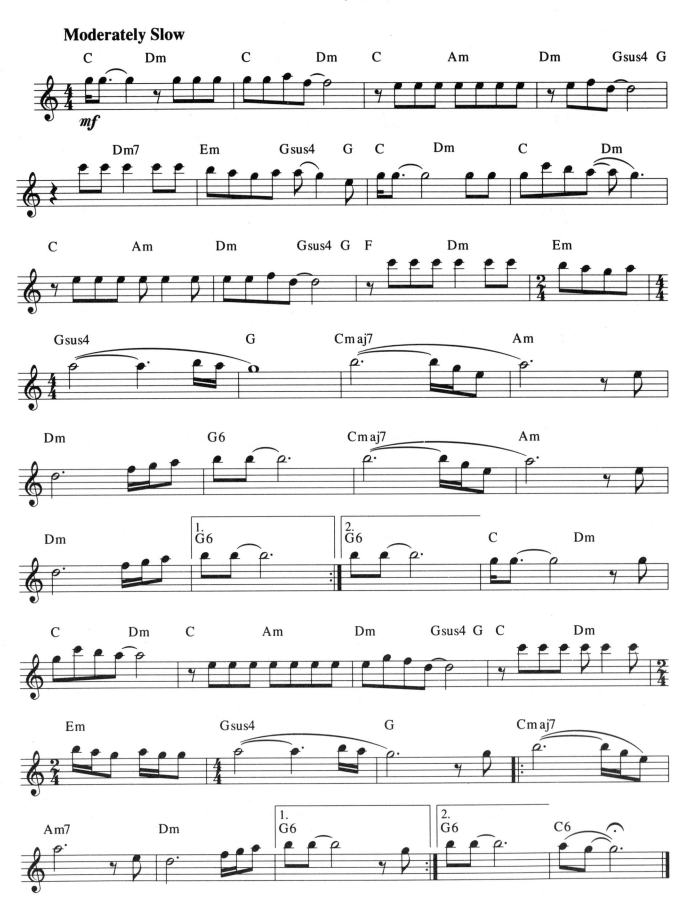

8/98 (31627)